HOMETOWN TALES
Beyond the Awning

also by Ed Vidler
East Aurora, From Under the Awning
printed 2003

copyright 2004 Edward W. Vidler
Robert Fisk, illustrator
all rights reserved
C. L. Thompson, editor and publisher

For reprint information:
Vidler's Five and Dime
676-694 Main Street
East Aurora, NY 14052
Toll Free 1-877-843-5377

"I Mopped the Floor With the Mayor" and "The
Last Ball Game" were previously
published in the *Buffalo News*

ISBN 0-9759700-1-1

printed in the United States of America

to Pat
and our "Eagle's Nest" family
all sixteen

Table of Contents

Acknowledgements

My wife, Pat, has again handled all my inane questions about spelling, history, and good taste. Her encouragement never stops even after reading these new stories countless times.

Thanks also to my E-mail pen pals who have had bits and pieces sent to them and never complained. Sometimes they even egged me on! Plus many others who were in the right place with the right comments and gave color and detail to these tales.

My editor, Cindy Thompson, who had the optimism and enthusiasm to make this second book come alive. Bob Fisk, the old sailor, who again caught the spirit of the stories in his original illustrations. Thanks to Joe Arimond, Martha Augat, Don Dayer, Doug Marky, Matt and Nita Orth, and Tim Thompson, who all helped by reading these tales in a less polished state.

And thanks to all of East Aurora for supplying the raw material for this book that covers a little of the Life, People, and Laughter of the hometown we all love.

Who Says I Eat Dog Food?

It was a quiet weekday morning at Fox's Deli. The usual cleaning, straightening and stocking up was going on as Mr. and Mrs. Fox waited on the customers, who were there not only to get a few groceries but hopefully a little gossip on the local happenings.

It was a peaceful moment of low confidential conversation amidst the homey odors that gave the place the atmosphere we can never recapture.

Suddenly, the front door banged open and in shuffled Old Coodge. A regular customer who, due to his occupation, made an unwelcome contribution to the aroma. Coodge eked out a living picking over old trash.

One of his best sources of income was the old Roycroft copper plates and bowls people would occasionally throw out. When melted down, they sold for a good price on the scrap metal market. No thought in that day and age was given to the idea of antiques, collectibles, or arts and crafts. As Coodge might have said, "Junk is Junk!"

But on this day Coodge had a mission to defend his honor. Conversation stopped when

Coodge walked to the counter and, in what could be described as a confrontational manner, demanded to know who was spreading the rumor that he was eating dog food.

Mr. Fox, being of the old school and mindful of the delicate ears of his customers, immediately stepped forward and said, "Why, Coodge, nobody here would say anything like that about you."

"Okay," said Coodge, "I don't ever want to hear it again. Now gimme a loaf of bread and a can of Alpo."

A Foot Too Close

When dealing with other people, everybody has their own style. Some like to shout from across the room while others like to get up close and personal.

As a clerk in a store, you communicate with and are confronted by all manner of personalities. This can involve lip reading and body language interpretation, for the not-too-close-to-me types, while what I call the "artful dodger" approach works best with the up-close-and-personal variety.

Mrs. Schlagel was what would have to be called the "in your face" type. Her hearing wasn't too good, so she had become a crowder, the better to hear you, and her voice was loud so that she got the attention she required. She also had a tendency, due to ill-fitting dentures, to lisp and spray, which made standing too close somewhat uncomfortable. Not like Niagara Falls, but moist at times.

I didn't really want to avoid her: she was interesting to talk to. Sometimes she had a story about a grandchild, a vacation trip, or some stunt her late husband had pulled. So, with years of experience, I had developed various subtle techniques to stay out of her spray. Stepping behind the counter used to work years ago, but nowadays counters aren't

built the same way. When sweeping the floor, I could use the broom to establish a space barrier. There were other methods, too. A clipboard or a couple of letters could also be held up in such a manner as to deflect the direct drenching. However, as with most plans or strategies, the system would sometimes fail.

One average business day, the old front door rattled open and in walked Mrs. Schlagel. Her loud questioning voice stopped me immediately, with no convenient counter to duck behind, no broom to defend my space, not even a scrap of protective paper to keep her at a dry distance.

A slow tactical retreat was my only chance, and it worked at first. But her pursuit was relentless, and then a slight hesitation on my part gave her the opportunity to accidentally step on my foot.

I was trapped. My quest to maintain a two-foot limit was defeated and her one-foot preference ruled the scene. I kept trying, without success, to pull my painfully trod-on, sneaker-clad foot from under her solid no-nonsense clog. At the same time I was trying to hold up my end of a pleasant conversation while leaning backward at a 45-degree angle.

She was still a foot too close.

Song From the Past

Early in the morning when the store first opens, there are no customers around, and the girls enjoy talking about family and friends and sometimes do a little reminiscing. Last Friday morning was no different, until somebody started to hum a long-forgotten tune, even trying to sing a couple of the verses. But memory failed and only a few half-remembered phrases were mumbled.

Then, from a corner of the basement, hidden by piles of merchandise, came a soft sweet voice, singing the old song with all the right words and tune. As the last words floated out, a little white-haired lady appeared with a knowing smile and twinkling eyes. She gave a timid nod of acknowledgment and briefly joined the laughter and chatter of her small audience.

Then, with a little wave of her hand, the shy stranger continued with her shopping, walking behind a stack of baskets and out of sight. A phone call interrupted any further questioning of the singer about that old familiar tune. Later, the girls wondered about their early morning visitor, but she was gone.

Funny, nobody saw her arrive or leave!

Kent & Roat's Closes

There are going out of business sales, and then there are GOING OUT OF BUSINESS sales!

Erwin & Alton Kent had taken over the business after the death of their father and his partner, Mr. Roat. In the late 1960s, small-town department/general stores were not the fastest growing or most lucrative retail businesses going, so after a short interval, the owners decided to close out the over-fifty-year-old operation. It was actually a good decision, as they both had interesting and successful careers in other fields.

But, oh my! What a Sale they put on!

The boys had been brought up in East Aurora with its small-town values of honesty, fairness and doing the right thing. Plus the training of their father, a merchant from the old school, where a Going Out of Business Sale is just that. You are going out of business. In a larger town or city, it can be a case of "take the money and run" before you set up shop a few blocks away.

But the Boys wanted to do it right, in keeping with their philosophy of honesty, fairness, etc., etc. So the first thing you do for a sale is to mark things down. Now, most professional

going-out-of-business promoters offer a small
discount, maybe 10%, to start things off, and
then give bigger discounts up to 50% when
the selection is not so good.

Not Erwin and Alton. They were dealing with their town, their relatives, neighbors, and friends.

They also had given out Brown Stamps for the entire fifty-plus-year period, instead of Green Stamps which were more common. So, on the first day of the sale, they offered a 50% discount on all items and double value on Brown stamps. It was a bargain hunter's paradise.

And oh Boy! What a mob scene! The first sign we had of the impending disaster (well, not really a disaster, more a feeding frenzy) was when a new Cadillac pulled up and parked in front of the store, and the driver ran into the store, leaving a woman sitting in the car. A minute later, he re-appeared with an armload of sport coats, tossed them on the hood, and started trying them on. His wife never even opened the window. She just sat there and nodded yes or no as each new jacket was tried on. The yes pile went into the car, and the no pile was returned to the store by the honest well-to-do car owner. Inside, he paid $5 each for his selections and drove off. The whole transaction took about three minutes. He had double parked, but he was honest.

Later, we saw an attractive younger woman hobbling out of Kent & Roat's, shaken

9

and tearful but with an armload of shoes. On closer inspection we noticed that she had on one high heeled pump and one black & white saddle shoe, thus the limp. While trying on shoes, she suddenly realized that the saddle shoe she had kicked off while trying on the pump, had been grabbed and tried on by another customer who disappeared into the crowd. Her solution was to limp out with six or eight pairs of shoes at $1 a pair. The heck with the bruises and tears. The prices were right.

The sale lasted another week or two. Kent & Roat's even had some depression glass in the basement in original boxes. This was before collectors were into that sort of stuff. Their complete stock of high-button shoes went to the Aurora Players wardrobe room for about 25 cents a pair.

If you look carefully at the front of the building where The Woolly Lamb and The Dress Shop are located, you may be able to see the names "Kent & Roat" etched in the old painted-over glass front.

The stories go on but one thing is for sure: Erwin and Alton put on one heck of a sale, the likes of which East Aurora will never see again.

The Cooperstown Incident

The Baseball Hall of Fame in Cooperstown, New York, had to be the destination point for every baseball-crazy kid in America. This was in the late thirties, before television. Our radio-listening imaginations, developed over the years tuning into Tom Mix, The Shadow, and Fibber McGee & Molly, were ready for the limited radio broadcasts that made heroes of the baseball players of the day.

We were on our way back from a family visit to Boston where we went to a baseball game and saw Ted Williams hit a home run. We cruised along Route 20 in our 1936 Studebaker, and the relatively new sign advertising "The Baseball Hall Of Fame" was just too inviting. Dad was a long-time fan, my brother was a complete baseball nut, and I figured it must be O.K. if my only two role models were so excited about Cooperstown.

So we turned towards the Mecca of Baseball, my parents agreeing that the extra $15 for a tourist home stay would be worth the educational value for the boys (Bob and me). It was interesting, but after looking at about 200 baseballs and bats and having the chance to sit in an old stadium seat from Ebbets field, my interest began to wane. One more look at Ty Cobb's bat, Lou Gerhig's mitt and Hans Wagner's shoes did it. We headed for our swank lodgings, a good night's sleep, then breakfast in a diner and the long drive home.

Breakfast in the diner was kind of fun. Rather than the whole family eating the same food like at home, we could each order our own meal. It could be bacon and eggs, pancakes, oatmeal, or even a jelly donut! As we entered the diner, we saw a sign mounted on the screen door that said: "DANGER Electricity." This was something new. Naturally, we had electricity, but a sign saying "danger" required some explanation.

All through breakfast, Dad gave us a lecture on the dangers of electricity, how you couldn't see it, how fast it could travel along a wire, how it could hurt you and, horror of horrors, how it could even kill you. Our stomachs full of food and heads full of dire warnings, Dad led us to the cashier and we all took one last look at the dreaded sign.

To reinforce the lesson and make the danger graphic, Dad said, "See, boys! The sign says 'Danger Electricity.' Never, ever put your hands on the wire. Like this."

With that, Dad placed his hand on the wire screen to emphasize the point. There was a loud sizzling "Whap!" Dad clutched his hand and, for the first time in our young lives, we heard him use actual swear words in a very emphatic way. In those days, swearing in public was not proper. To make it worse, this was a Sunday morning, and so Dad apologized in every direction, to everyone within hearing distance, and we sort of scuttled out the door, Dad still clutching his hand.

We got in the car and only then did we realize that dad actually swore! Now, this was really something. Mom didn't seem too mad and Dad was still muttering and not about to correct us again, so we got in the back seat and giggled. We finally just lay down and roared. Even the folks got to laughing.

Later, Dad said he really got a shock and had trouble driving for a few minutes. We figured that the owner was not too familiar with electricity and just ran the full house current through the screen to kill flies.

So what did we learn at Cooperstown? Not much, but we never forgot the first time we heard Dad swear.

The Hitching Post

It was the last one on Main Street. Slate, about five feet high, it had a ring on top. In the heyday of the horse, it was just one of many that stood along most of the streets in East Aurora.

However, this was our hitching post, because it stood in front of the house we were raised in at 771 Main Street. I remember the post being used about three times, by the same older woman who drove a horse and buggy into town to shop. Even at that time, in 1933, it was a novelty for us little kids to see a real horse and buggy on the streets here in town. Not only that, but as we watched, an elderly lady dressed in a long dark dress and hat would step down out of the buggy and walk around the horse, tying it to the hitching post. This was a Currier & Ives picture that most only see in calendars and greeting cards.

Later, she would walk up Main Street with her bags of groceries and set them in the back of the buggy, much like the rear of a pick-up truck. She would again walk around the buggy and horse to the post, untie the horse, and step up into the buggy. Then she gathered the reins, sort of clucked to the horse, and made a U-turn to drive back out East Main Street.

After she stopped driving her buggy into town, the old post stood there for years, never to be used again. As happens with all relics of bygone eras, the inevitable happened and we found the old post lying by the curb.

There was no mention in the local press, no preservationist asking for government funds to repair or replace our post. It just laid there. Whether it was eventually hauled away or just got covered with the sands of time (in this case, road dirt), our hitching post was gone.

The end of an era, yes? But ah, the memories!

Core of the Business

The collection started back in the 1930s. Originally, the cores were strong, sturdy, and perfectly round. Then, during the war years, things changed. The thickness of the material was reduced, then the quality cheapened, and finally, with restrictions on shipping, the rolls were compressed so that more would fit in a case, which distorted their previously uniform shape. The collection continued to grow, but the symmetry was never the same.

We are talking about one of the most unusual and useless collections of toilet paper cores ever assembled. Once they were rid of their burden of toilet paper, Dad would stack them pyramid-style on a shelf in the lavatory. You could see how uniform the rolls were in the bottom rows, and how they changed during WWII as the materials and packing declined. A few salesmen would comment on the unusual collection and its steady growth whenever they used what would later be called the "executive wash room."

Then, as a result of a county health department inspection, we had to do some carpentry and duct work in the wash room. In one of those impetuous decisions of youth, my brother and I cleaned out the room and discarded the entire collection. When Dad saw the result of our work, he was stunned. Twenty years worth of toilet paper cores down the drain, so to speak.

Disaster struck soon after, as business dropped off for a couple of years. Having realized our mistake, we started the collection again. Now that we had more employees, it grew faster than ever. Business eventually got better too! Ten years later, the wash room was again inspected and found deficient. This time we needed an asphalt tile floor.

Meanwhile, we are not so impetuous nor as youthful, but the inspector's word is still law. So out went the collection, although it really didn't have the character of the pre-war collection. Oddly enough, again disaster struck, with business dropping off for a couple of years.

The inspections continued. This last time, we needed a sign over the door to tell us what we had been doing in that little room for 50 years. Now our impetuous youth is well behind us, but we put up the sign with this vital bit of washroom wisdom and cleaned out the collection for the third time. And another disaster! Business fell off. We reacted as any sane businesspeople would – we started up the collection again.

Now could it be, should it be, would it be that there is a direct correlation between the number of toilet paper rolls in the collection and the volume of our business? Is it possible that this is the "core of the business?"

Cannons on Main Street

When I was a kid, there were two cannons in East Aurora. One was a World War I howitzer on wheels that stood at the Circle. It was fairly well maintained, probably by the American Legion, and painted silver. It became what would now be called an attractive nuisance, fun to play on until either time or vandalism loosened some of the parts.

Finally, some kid climbed out on the barrel, and it swung down and squished him. How badly he was hurt we never heard, but we agreed that to be squished by a cannon sounded pretty bad. As little kids we imagined all kinds of blood and gore. Considering the times, if he wasn't hurt too badly, his folks probably yelled at him for breaking the cannon. Whatever the case, the cannon disappeared and the circle became a garden spot maintained by the Garden Club.

The other cannon was located next to the middle school and looked like something that might have been used during the Civil War or on a ship. It was a big fat thing mounted on a stone or cement pedestal. Probably black at one time, it had become weathered, pitted, and corroded, and was best described as cannon-colored. It wasn't much of a challenge

20

to climb, but it did make a nice, rather chilly seat, if cannon-sitting was your thing.

World War II came along, and scrap metal was needed for the war effort. All types of metal were collected, but copper was in particularly short supply. Many a priceless old Roycroft hand-hammered vase, lamp, or tray was consigned to the scrap metal heap in a patriotic fervor that made light of such sacrifice. Still, the old cannon just stood there until somebody must have realized that here was a really big supply of metal. It was probably iron, not copper, but it must have weighed hundreds of pounds.

One night, the cannon disappeared. It might have had historical significance, but nobody knew. We couldn't remember if there was even a plaque mounted on it giving pertinent historical details.

Was it melted down to be made into bombs? Or was it spirited away to be hidden or buried so that later generations could discover it and puzzle over its history?

Random Act of Kindness

A random act of kindness was committed on County Route #678 near Royal Oaks, on a Sunday afternoon in September, when we were hundreds of miles from home.

My wife Pat and I were driving from a family reunion to our son's house in New Jersey, when we had our first flat tire in about thirty years. There was that almost forgotten thump-thump, a wobbly slow stop, and two rather disheartened seventy-year-olds were stuck. What to do? The tire-changing routine was only a memory for old backs and arthritic hands.

Pat whipped out her cell phone and dialed AAA for roadside service. It proved difficult in that we didn't know exactly where we were. The trunk was open and I supposed we looked kind of perplexed as we tried to figure out which mat to move and how to get out the spare tire that was hidden under our luggage.

Along came a black pick-up truck, out stepped a strapping young guy in a white T-shirt, and he offered to help. We said, no, thanks, we were trying AAA, but he was pleasantly insistent, so we gratefully accept-ed. He expertly emptied the trunk, removed the tire and mini jack, crawled under the car, placed the jack in the right spot, removed the lugs, and had the wheel ready to remove.

But there was one problem! That wheel was not about to come off. Our Good Samaritan hopped back into his truck and dashed off to his house for liquid wrench, a two-by-four, and a mallet. We didn't even have time to wonder if he was really coming back before he was back and the tire was changed. We were ready to be on our way, and all this in about 15 minutes. It would have taken us half an hour to read the directions on how to assemble the jack and place it under the car.

After a hasty hand shake, an offer of money was made and vehemently refused. He said it was a "random act of kindness" and we should pass it on, and off zoomed our benefactor. To our regret, we never got his name or even his license number.

It just goes to prove that there are some wonderful people on the highway of life if you are lucky enough to meet them.

Koenig's Collision

Have you ever lived next door to a surgeon who works in a big hospital? They're generally confident, successful, possibly a little aloof, with emotions in control. Not the Good Old Doc type, who lives and works in our little village. There is a difference!

Our next-door neighbor was an eye surgeon, Dr. Koenig. As Dad used to say, "He was the perfect neighbor, we hardly knew him." But we did observe him, whether he was shouting precise instructions at Hans, the gardener; directing Laura, the maid, ordering her around as (we imagined) he might have browbeaten a nurse at the hospital; or telling Mrs. Koenig how to raise their only daughter, Ann Rae. Mrs. Koenig could shout as loud as he could, and we assumed that most family decisions were pretty much a stand-off.

Being a positive physician (and all physicians have to be positive), Dr. Koenig drove with a positive manner. At an early age, my brother and I were warned to stay out of the driveway if the good doctor got in his car. You must remember, in those days before liability laws and health insurance, it was more like a jungle. And Dr. Koenig drove with the attitude

that anything that dared get in his way deserved whatever it got. Therefore, if Koenig was backing out of the driveway, we had to look out, because he never did!

The morning of the collision was normal. There was the creaking of the garage door being opened (no automatic door openers in those days), the slamming of the car door, and Dr. Koenig's car roaring into reverse. He was probably late for work. He looked neither to the right, left or rear. As was his habit, he just backed.

And as usual, his car didn't slow down – until it hit the horse-drawn garbage wagon that had paused at the foot of his driveway! The car sort of bounced back up the drive. There seemed to be no injuries, although the car was bruised and had acquired some of the wagon's offensive cargo. The garbage wagon appeared no worse for the collision, but it could not have been much more bruised or dirty than it already was.

Out of the car stormed the doctor. This was to be his finest hour. He shouted and ranted at the garbage wagon and the garbage man. Even the horse was a target, as he vented his rage and finely honed sarcasm at the sheer stupidity of all those around him. The garbage wagon and horse never moved, and the garbage man was speechless.

Hurling one final insult, Dr. Koenig climbed back into his car, jammed it in reverse, and stepped on the gas, slamming into the wagon again, his head snapping back in stupefied surprise!

The unruffled garbage man shrugged his shoulders and drove horse and wagon away, leaving the scene of Koenig's collision with more dignity than did the good doctor.

Saving Dad

We were always fortunate to have interesting and different vacations all during our growing-up years. Trips to Boston to see our Vidler relatives were always exciting, with views of ships and the ocean from Uncle Fred's lighthouse. This is probably where Bob first developed his interest in the sea.

Here in East Aurora we spent a wonderful childhood surrounded by White relatives. However, our parents felt that travel and different experiences were fun and educational. So we took a trip across the U.S.A. in 1941, but we also stayed at Harvey Abbot's farm in Java, visited an Aunt in New York City, and rented a cottage on Cuba Lake. Here Bob took his first walk with his future wife Lynn, I drowned worms in Cuba Lake, and we both saved Dad's life.

Dad, Bob, and I had been fishing and sort of killing time until Tink, Leota, Lynn, and Laurie (Dave wasn't born yet) arrived for a visit. The sound of their big Buick on the gravel driveway announced their arrival, so Dad paddled us over to the dock and told me to jump out. I did and started to walk up to the cabin when Dad informed me that when you get out of a boat you take a rope with you and tie the boat to the dock. So back I went. He threw the rope, and I missed it! No problem, I just leaned over and grabbed the side of the boat and pulled it over near the dock. Bob, who was still seated in the boat, then leaned over and grabbed the dock, also. With the support of the two willing but inept sailors, Dad swung his good leg up on the dock.

Things were looking good and we were impressing the Freemans with our seamanship. Then what probably happened was that Bob was looking at Lynn and I forgot what I was supposed to be doing, so our death-like grips on the boat and dock were relaxed and boat and dock slowly separated, with one of Dad's feet on the dock and the other in the boat. As the boat drifted away, there came a great roar out of our usually quiet Dad. Arms flailing, he went over backward into the lake, between the dock and the boat.

He sputtered to the surface and his now very attentive, anxious-to-please sons hurried to his rescue. I was on the dock and Bob was still in the boat, and each of us grabbed one of Dad's legs. With a youthful heave we each pulled a leg out of the water, while Dad held on to the dock with one hand and the boat with the other. Naturally, Bob pulled the leg he had into the boat while I hauled the other

31

leg up on the dock. There was another roar as Dad lost his handhold. Back in to the lake went Dad!

When he popped to the surface this time, his instructions were rather grim. "O.K. boys, let go of my legs. The water is only three feet deep. I'll walk to shore."

Snow Scalloping

No kidding, East Aurora's sidewalks were plowed with a horse-drawn plow. The last one was used down around Parkdale, Willow, and Shearer and Main in the 1950s. It gave East Aurora a real Norman Rockwell look as you saw the driver, wooden plow, and horse plodding along. The horse-drawn plow was slow moving and pushed the snow aside in a nice sharp ridge. The side facing the freshly cleared sidewalk had a flat-packed, low wall-like appearance.

We lived on Parkdale then and saw lots of kids walk to school every day. Much more colorful and interesting than seeing three or four school buses roar past. As with all school kids, there was a variety of ages, heights, clothing, and personalities represented in this passing parade. Some walked in twos, some in groups, some with parents, and then there were the loners. All moved along in a somewhat purposeful manner, to get to school on time.

Now there are loners and there are happy wanderers. The wanderers were the most fun to watch! They might be a trial to parents and teachers, who wanted them to be responsible

and on time, but time was not a problem for them, not when there was so much to look at and examine. Whether it was flowers in the spring, a cat sitting on a porch, or a pretty leaf in the fall.

But following a horse-drawn snow plow was the ultimate for our favorite wanderer. On this special day, not only did she enjoy the snowy saunter but the sharply etched ridge of snow proved too tempting.

So with a measured gait and eye for design, our little friend carefully sat on the plowed up ridge of snow, again and again. It was a step and a sit, a step and a sit all the way down Parkdale to school.

When the plow and she had passed, it looked like the edge of Grandmother's pie crust, and the best bit of scalloped-edge snowplow ridges we had ever seen.

Tannery Brook Yacht Club

Tannery Brook was probably the best water playground in East Aurora. Of course, Hamlin Park had recreational equipment and supervision that was ahead of the times, especially when it opened in the 1930s. But for unsupervised fun, you couldn't beat The Creek, a.k.a. Tannery Brook.

There were bubbling gas springs in the shale that could be lighted when you put a glass bottle with the bottom knocked out over the escaping bubbles. The giant willows hanging over the creek were ideal for tree houses that the older kids had built. A handy dump on East Fillmore Avenue supplied lots of glass bottles: floated down the creek, they made great targets for rock heaving.

Occasionally, the dump supplied round oak tables of Roycroft vintage for rolling down to the creek. They made nice round rafts until they busted up or floated out of reach. But my friends and I finally came to the conclusion that for real enjoyment on the creek, we needed a boat. We decided we would form the Tannery Brook Yacht Club.

To build a boat you needed wood and nails, and our only source was old orange crates. Properly broken up, they yielded a supply of both. You just had to be careful not to split the wood when you pulled out the nails, and then you had to spend a little time to straighten them out. So in short order we had the materials and the rest of the summer to build our boat.

We didn't bother with plans – we just started nailing. The result was a coffin-shaped box that was not particularly water tight. No problem: we figured we would just cover it with old canvas material from a worn-out store awning and slap on a coat of tar from a left-over bucket of roof-patching stuff, and we would be ready for the launch.

But then somebody said that if you soaked a wooden boat in water, it would swell up enough to seal off all the leaks. We thought that was a good idea, and would save us time, too, as no canvas or tar would be needed. All we had to do was pick up the boat from its dry dock next to Kelver Court, and walk it across Main Street and down Pine Street to the creek.

After some research, we christened our creation "The Conepate," which meant "skunk" in the old dictionary.

Anyway, when it was time to put it in the water, the three of us bent down and got a good grip for a hearty heave ho, but nothing happened. That sucker was so heavy we couldn't budge it.

No problem! Our ingenuity was endless. We would build a cart using old baby buggy wheels from the dump, and then roll the boat to the creek. But then the wheels broke! We finally admitted we did have a problem. By then it was the middle of a hot, dry summer, and the creek didn't have much water left in it.

We gave up the idea of the Tannery Brook Yacht Club and, undaunted, decided to have a Viking Funeral Pyre.

So we called in all our friends and, with great difficulty and much grunting, moved the Conepate out into the empty field just off Kelver Court, took a few East Aurora Advertisers and maybe a couple of old Philistines, and started our fire.

Being a nice summer day with lots of dry grass, conditions were just right for one of that summer's better grass fires. Brassy and George Fisher came running out of Kelver's garage with brooms and shovels to help us try to beat out the fire. But the fire had too much head start and too much fuel and stayed ahead of us, even with the grown-ups' help.

Finally Kenny Fones pulled up with the East End Active Hose Pumper and soaked down the blackened remains of the Conepate.

Water! That had been the Conepate's problem all summer. First not enough of it, which meant we couldn't rule the creek. Then too much of it, which cut short our Viking funeral (but at least the village didn't burn down).

Its name had turned out to be prophetic. As for boat-building, we were skunked in the end.

Pies, and Pies

There is nothing like Mom's homemade apple pie. Forlorn WWII songs have been written and sung about this favorite concoction. Nobody doesn't love it. The idea of a new car and Mom's homemade apple pie created images of America at its best.

A true pie lover will even use Mom's homemade apple pie as the ultimate standard by which all other desserts are measured. Tension in new marriages often increases or decreases due to the comparison of the bride's pie-baking ability with Mom's. The success of many a small-town restaurant depends on the chef's flair for almost duplicating Mom's homemade apple pie.

However, there is a world beyond Mom's apple pie, and that is the pie eating contest. This endeavor requires something almost as good but messier, namely blueberry pie. Properly presented, the pie smears all over the contestants' faces and stains their clothes. This creates good photo opportunities for the newspapers but is not too thrilling when you go home and have Mom tell you what she thinks of the mess and the people who thought up the idea of the contest.

A good pie-eating contest is great entertainment at family-oriented picnics, and a good fundraiser for charitable organizations that creates lasting memories for the participants.

Being a fast eater and gulper, I was a natural for entering the pie-eating contest at the East Aurora Boys Club fundraiser in 1939. It seemed easy! All I had to do was eat lots of my second-most-favorite pie (blueberry) and be champ in the 11-to-12-year-old category.

After the first two or three gulps I was way ahead of the picky nibblers. All I had to do was plunge in face first for one more gargantuan gulp. But my enthusiasm was my downfall as my nose met pie plate with surprising force beneath the gloppy purple goo.

I bleed easily. That nose battering pie dive resulted in a rather disgusting last bite. Now, there is a limit as to what even a Boys Club Charter Member could eat, and bloody blueberry pie was not one of them.

I wasn't the champ, and blueberry is still my second-most-favorite pie. If it had been Mom's homemade apple pie, I would have won, no matter what!

Grandmother's Cookies

My brother, Bob, who is older than I, remembers Grandmother's cookies with great fondness. He will go so far as to say they were the greatest. He describes in detail their wonderful flavor, large size, and softness. My memories of Grandmother's cookies are a little different.

I remember Grandmother's cookies as the soak-'em-in-milk-they-may-soften-eventually variety. If you want to be generous, you could call them crispy. I considered them hard, with a faint taste of burned bacon. You have to remember that this was during the depression, when lard was expensive but used bacon grease was cheap and plentiful.

So, in a matter of a few depressing depression years, Grandmother's cookies went from (if Bob can be believed) tasty, soft mounds of mouth-filling delights to greasy, flinty, tooth-threatening relics of their former glory. I ate them along with her homemade candied orange peel.

With these two snacks under my belt I would head home, not to visit Grandmother for another week or so. Sometimes I wondered if she wanted me to come back, but then she'd bake some bread, just for me, and I knew she did.

Now I don't want my cousin's wrath descending on me, but cookies and oranges were never my favorite food, and that depression-era experience didn't help. I'd rather remember Grandmother for her bread baking. The smell of fresh baked bread still brings back memories of Grandmother's house. But not her cookies.

The Steel-Springed Steed

A spring horse was the ideal gift for a three-year-old who wanted and needed action. It was fool-proof, easy to mount, and got all its motion from the rider. You just got on it and started rocking, bouncing, and twisting. There were four sturdy springs, one on each corner of the metal frame. These springs attached to four hooks that protruded from the rounded molded body of the horse. It seemed safe and gave just the proper support and bouncy action that all three-year-olds like.

Christmas morning, the horse (actually it was more pony-sized) was unwrapped. In one swift leap, my son Don hopped on the saddle and was on his way to hours of fun and excitement, just as the toy advertisement had promised.

There was one small difference: Faw Faw. She was his Grandmother, who picked up her unusual nickname from another grandson. In those ancient time it was not unusual for adult children to use their mother's first name as a term of endearment. Florence was her name, but the grandson, about three at the time, could not pronounce her name. The closest he could come was Faw Faw, which in baby talk sounded kind of cute.

Now, Faw Faw, as she had come to be called, was cautious. She knew the principles of Murphy's Law long before it was recognized by the rest of the world. To her, the sight of an active little grandson bouncing along on a toy supported by four springs was an accident waiting to happen.

So, she raised the alarm. Tactfully put, she said, "He'll kill himself on that thing!" It was equally tactfully explained to her that there would be no injury. Just think of it: here was a toy, designed by American engineers, produced by an American toy company, and sold in the family store. How could that be dangerous?

Meanwhile, little Donald was having the time of his life, as he learned how to make the spring action of the horse bounce him higher and faster.

She made one last dire warning, and then we skillfully turned her attention and concern aside. After all, it was Christmas and kids were supposed to have fun and excitement. Right?

Just then, there was sharp sound, something like the plucking of a giant bass guitar string. There before our astonished eyes

sailed Donald, flipping and twisting like a limp rag doll, as if shot from a giant sling. His wide-eyed landing draped him unceremoniously over the old family couch on the other side of the room.

There was no injury, but family pride and the American way of life took a beating. There sat Faw Faw, her eyebrows raised in a knowing and understanding way. To her credit, she said nothing!

Real Roar

When icy arctic winds roar in across Lake Erie in early winter, before the lake has frozen, we in Western New York get lake-effect snowstorms. They can be pretty serious, especially if you are out in the middle of one, with its white-outs and rapid accumulation of snow. And they're concentrated: two or three miles to the left or right of the blizzard's center, you could be basking in sunshine.

East Aurora has seen many lake-effect snows, and we were the center of such a storm about 30 years ago. Although the sky was clear at midnight, over 24 inches of the heavy white stuff had fallen by morning. With a storm like that, the first thing you do, if you have school-age kids, is to see if schools are closed. Then you get out into it, to challenge the elements, if you can.

It was still snowing when my son Don and I put on our new snowshoes and walked up the middle of Main Street. There wasn't a car in sight, and just one lone cross-country skier, Fred Kitson of Fillmore Avenue, doing the same thing that we were: seeing what it was like to be one of the first to venture outdoors.

Such deep snow has a muffling effect on any sound. There was little wind at the moment, so the trees were covered with a beautiful white blanket of snow that made the town look like a Norman Rockwell Christmas card. Other than our voices, it was all stillness and solitude. We felt very isolated in our little village, cut off from the rest of the world.

Another snowshoer was coming around the corner of Main and Pine as we made our way closer to the Store. It was Gerhard Neumaier, and we spoke briefly with him before we noticed five huge trucks parked down the block, in front of the Aurora Theater. It was snowing so hard we couldn't make out what they were.

Out of one of the trucks stepped a lone figure in jeans and a T-shirt, certainly not dressed for our weather. He looked up the street and back the other way, before looking down at the map in his hands, the snow gathering on his bare forearms. Curious, we moved closer.

When he saw us, he called out, asking the name of the town. Don spoke up before I could, saying proudly, "East Aurora!" The man looked back at his map and asked, of no one in particular, why the heck they would

route his trucks through such a god-forsaken place on his way back to South Carolina.

Circus! Who ever heard of a circus in the middle of a blizzard! Don and I looked at each other, wondering if he was crazy or just trying to play a trick on us. Just then, the snowy quiet was shattered by the real roar of a lion.

Murder Confession at Wally's

Hod worked at the lumber mill on Oakwood Avenue for years, six days a week. He walked home for lunch every day when the mill whistle blew at noon, and he trudged down Oakwood again for supper with his wife, Molly, after the 5 o'clock whistle blew. Saturday night was different: after the quitting-time whistle, he had a few beers at Wally's before the hike home. His daily routine was pretty much controlled by that mill whistle. Even emergencies would involve the whistle. As a volunteer fireman, he would listen for the series of blasts that gave the general location of the fire.

Molly's life was controlled by the mill whistle, too. Her days were spent on the endless cycle of housework, punctuated by the whistle's shrill shriek. The only days that were free from the whistle's dictates were summer Sundays (unless there was a fire), when Hod would take Molly to Hamlin Park to watch the town team play baseball.

Hod and Molly had a good life, but quiet, since they had no kids.

Of course, they both had their friends and

families, and Molly had the diversions of the mailman delivering the daily mail, the ice man and his three weekly deliveries, and the visits of the bakery man who stopped in to deliver bread on Tuesday and Friday.

Now, Molly was attractive, peppy, and fun loving. She was thought of as a good and dutiful wife, until that fateful summer in the 1920s. No one knew if maybe the drudgery got to her. Whatever the case, a little hanky-panky appeared to have developed with the bread delivery man, who was from the city and obviously swept poor Molly away with his fast talk and city airs.

Rumors began to spread as the neighbors noticed the bread delivery truck's lingering stops. Finally, all the boys at the mill knew about his domestic situation, except poor Hod. It was agreed that he should know. The problem was, how to tell him? Nobody wanted to be the one to break the news. A scheme was devised to blow the mill whistle early on Tuesday or Friday, so that Hod would arrive home ahead of schedule. He would learn the truth, without anyone having to actually tell him, and hopefully he would nip the affair in the bud.

It seemed like a good plan. However, a lot of good plans have unintended consequences.

No one at the mill knew that beneath Hod's plodding manner was a man with the morals of a saint and the temper of a sinner.

The prearranged early whistle blew, and the unsuspecting Hod went home to the sight of a delivery wagon in his yard and the afore-mentioned hanky-panky in the bedroom. With no apparent commotion, Hod took his shot gun and dispatched the offending parties. He then walked back up Oakwood to Wally's, sat at the corner table, and ordered a round of beers. He requested the presence of a sheriff and, once the sheriff had arrived, confessed his crime to one and all at Wally's that astonishing afternoon.

The Second Buzzing

Every kid who joined the Air Corps during WWII had the dream of becoming a pilot and buzzing the old home town. It happened here in East Aurora!

One of the enlistees (he was a great punter on the high school football team) actually trained in California and became a B-17 bomber pilot. Naturally, the only way to get the planes to Europe was to fly them there from the west coast. The flight plan was to go from the west coast to the east coast, and then across the Atlantic. Our East Aurora native did just what any East Aurora kid would do. He had his navigator head for the old home town.

Now, we had been buzzed before by three Bell Airacobra fighter planes, but this was a B-17 with four huge motors. We had heard roars before, but this was deafening. For maximum results the best route was to bring the plane in low out about where Route 400 crosses Main Street. Of course there was no 400 then, but there were a couple of big estates out around Cook Road that any local would recognize from the air.

The captain brought this big sucker in at tree top level right down the entire length of

Main Street, east to west, circled out over the Knox Estate and around the crooked water tower at 20A and Transit Road, and buzzed Main Street again. Then he circled out over Wales Center and made his final pass over Main Street.

The town was a-buzz (no pun intended) about this stunt that had scared and delighted us with this display of our military might. Official sources were contacted, flight plans were reviewed, regulations checked, but no records were ever found to indicate any unauthorized military action over East Aurora that memorable day.

We all knew we had been buzzed by one of our own as he went off to war.

Lost in the Podonque Cemetery

In the hills just outside Rushford there is an old cemetery. Driving down the road to Hume, you can see the lovely wrought-iron gate with a sign arching over the entrance. The white painted letters of the sign spelled out PODONQUE CEMETERY.

We drove around the gate. For some reason nobody drives under the sign. Then we followed the grass-centered dirt road past a corn field to the top of the hill and approached the ancestral burial ground of the Williams, my Grandmother's side of the family.

When we arrived at this marble and granite orchard of old familiar names there was no place to park or turn around. The only wide place, in what is best defined as a grass covered lane, was occupied by truck and trailer for the lawn mower equipment that was being operated by the one-woman cemetery maintenance company. Our problem was quickly and easily recognized by the now curious grass cutter. She hailed us and gave directions. Just follow the road down around the cemetery. She sort of waved her hands in a circular motion to indicate the route.

Seemed easy enough! We drove on down the very grassy lane to the end of the row of carved granite tombstones. Ahead the lane gave away to a couple of narrowing dirt tracks, with plenty of grass in the center to wipe off any remaining grease and oil on the bottom of our car. Our only choice seemed to be to keep on driving, so we drove and drove until we figured we must be approaching Hard Scrabble Road, which parallels the Hume Road.

But it sure didn't seem like we were going around the Podonque Cemetery. As the dirt tracks disappeared into the now untamed underbrush and our car was being brushed by the branches of wild blackberries, we arrived at a true dead end. Facing us was a twenty-foot cliff of dirt and rocks, an abandoned gravel pit. Eventually, with backing up and the careful cramping of the wheels, we managed to turn around and go back up the only escape route available. Then we back tracked what surely must have been a country mile, but not around the cemetery.

Safe at last, we finally returned to Podonque and civilization and the frantically waving lawn lady. She patiently explained and showed us city slickers the nice grass-covered driveway, which did in fact circle the very small cemetery. We got out of the car and self-consciously bent over to look at the dates on some of the headstones. Luckily, the Williams name was very prominent and we did find some familiar names, hoping it made us appear capable of some mature behavior.

As we drove away, I glanced in the rear view mirror. Our benefactor was waving her hands in the now familiar circular pattern, but with one finger pointing at her temple. I figured it was a Podonque Good-Bye and Good Luck gesture!

Jest Set-a-Spell

Late winter, early spring, you know the feeling of unrest. You're tired of snow, and it's too early to garden, but in Western New York it's time for maple syrup making. For an interesting change of pace, some us head out of town for some action in Curriers, New York.

Now, Curriers is where the Chaffee-Curriers Road splits off the Curriers Road. If the roads were more traveled or they were big highways, they might be called the Curriers Interchange. Currier's other mark of distinction is the lone street light that casts its warm night-time glow over the heart of the commercial district.

The only building of significance is the Curriers Grange Hall, circa A.D. something or other, and the sign that sprouts this time every year announcing a Maple Syrup Social. We noticed it years ago. Nicely hand lettered, it announces two dates, one in March and one in April.

Odie, an old friend and Curriers resident who looks like a rough-hewn Charlton Heston, told us all about the Maple Syrup Social and asked us to come on out and join the citizens of Curriers and the Grange

Members. That's all the invitation we needed, suffering as we were from a mild attack of cabin fever.

Getting there was easy. You just drive out the Curriers Road until you see a bunch of cars parked around the Grange Hall. Inside, we were warmly greeted by Odie. We bought our tickets and got in line as they cooked freshly mixed pancakes (they don't start mixing them until you come in the door). Three big pancakes and a couple of sausages are handed to you hot off the griddle.

The main hall, where we ate, has the warmth of an old well-used dining room that could have dropped out of time from three generations ago. The table was set family-style with plenty of fresh maple syrup, butter, baking powder biscuits, hard-boiled eggs, dill pickles, and coffee, tea, milk and juice.

So naturally we started eating, and we tried everything, even the pickles. It's an old dietary axiom that you should eat something sour with something sweet, in this case, pickles with maple syrup. Surprisingly, the combination tastes pretty good after the initial shock. Trying to figure out what the two ingredients might do when they hit your stomach could be of concern for the less adventurous eater.

We ate and talked, were offered seconds on the pancakes (nobody at our table had any), and talked some more. We were stuffed, so the table was cleared and out came bowls or cups of snow and larger bowls of hot maple syrup. Now came the best part. We were ready for the final bit of down-at-the-sugar-shanty fun.

A couple of old timers then explained the art of making jack wax, which is done by dribbling the hot syrup onto the cold snow and watching it turn into a soft taffy-like maple candy. It is sweet and delicious, and a little goes a long way.

Step two: Take the remaining syrup and stir like mad for a few minutes and watch carefully as it changes color and consistency until a soft sugar develops. Then you pour it onto wax paper so that it cools and hardens slightly. This we took home for later consumption.

It was an evening of fun with a slice of Americana you could only find in a hamlet like Curriers. By now we were not only stuffed but getting sleepy. Just as we were leaving, Odie stopped by our table. We said thanks for a pleasant evening and we would be on our way home so that they could clean up the dining room.

Odie looked put out and said, "Wait a minute, you didn't read the sign out front." I frowned, trying to recall exactly what it did say. I couldn't remember anything beyond the event and its time and date, so I finally said, "Well, what *does* it say?"

He answered, waving his hand at the people still sitting around the dining room, "It says Maple Sugar *Social*. Now you jest set-a-spell, and talk."

Flute Finale

Music, the ultimate art to raise the spirits of mankind. Or the bane of the less artistic. The gifted and talented can't get enough, while the no-talents are force-fed the stuff in the hope that some culture will rub off on them.

Unfortunately, I fall into the latter category. A talent for blowing air across the top of a coke bottle or a large jug that held apple cider gave me the know-how to make a sound on a flute when Mr. Fattey placed it in my hands. He was looking for recruits for the high school band, and he needed flute players. I was just glad he didn't need tuba players that day! The tubas were a dilly to haul home for practice and then to march with at the football games.

In my innocent joy, I informed my parents that Mr. Fattey said I could learn to play the flute, with a little practice. "A little practice" stretched out into five years. Special private lessons and band and orchestra practice ground on from year to year. Band and orchestra could be faked while Nancy and Betty carried the tune, but private lessons were solos for Mr. Fattey's unfortunate ears only.

Now, it's not easy to cram for music lessons. Proper preparation takes hours of tedious

noodling along the pages of music that have to be learned. Yet somehow I always managed to skip practice until about an hour before the lesson. My customary cramming resulted in a tired embouchure – that's what they call the way you have to hold your lips to make any sound come out of that delightful little instrument. So I would arrive at my lesson with an anguished embouchure. The all-knowing Mr. Fattey would ask, "Ed, you seem over-tired. Have you been practicing too much?" Yeah, right!

This went on for five long years, until that fateful Sunday when Mom was in church, and I was home with Dad, who was reading the Sunday paper. Now, Dad was probably about 55, and that's old when you are 16. Anyhow, I decided it was time to show Dad that I could play "the Thing," which is what he called it. I began to play, and the Sunday paper kind of trembled. In my innocence, I assumed it was because of Dad's advanced years. So, noodling along, I rendered trills and scales, tunes and tones. Although why a flute has to trill, I will never know.

I thought I was putting on a pretty good show! Then the trembling paper slowly lowered, and Dad said in a very controlled voice,

"You know, Ed, you sound the same on that damn thing as you did the day we bought it."

I was stunned! I had only heard Dad swear one other time, ever. But after a moment, I recovered. "Dad," I answered in my squeaky teen-age voice, "you're right!"

I had been playing the flute for years, reluctantly, because I thought he liked hearing it. He had been listening for the same long, torturous time because he thought I liked playing it.

Monday morning I walked into the Music Room and announced to Mr. Grant (Mr. Fattey had retired), in my most diplomatic yet squeaky voice, "I quit!"

What a relief! No more practice, no more concerts, no more marching, no more tired embouchure. Thanks, Dad! And I think he was just as glad.

The Last Ball Game

If you played baseball like most of us did in the 1930s and '40s, it was just a matter of finding someone who had a baseball and bat.

A variety of old gloves usually appeared. The diamond was in any open space, and foul lines were established by line of sight with objects such as trees, bushes, and corners of buildings. Bases could be rocks, rags, or rubbish.

The field didn't matter much. Eighty percent of the game involved arguments over balls, strikes, who was safe, and fair or foul balls, depending on the established line of sight. With all the confusion, who could possibly remember one game from the other?

After the arrival of the AARP years, the challenge of playing one more game can be memorable. It was a long time ago, but I can still remember the last game I played.

At a family picnic, the traditional pickup game was started and, due to a lack of players, I was invited to play ball. I'd figured my throwing, hitting and running days were over, but Gee, it was sure flattering to think that they wanted me to play.

So at 58, I was the oldest player on the field. The rest of the teams were made up of the usual family groups ages 6 to 36. The old throw, catch, hit and run routine looked familiar and by golly, I was actually going to play, new glasses and all.

Fielding was easy – nobody hit the ball in my direction. Then it was my turn at bat. The first pitch came in, and the ball looked as big as a watermelon! I missed by a foot, darn new glasses.

But luck was with me, plus a very slow pitch, and I was able to get a hit. So what if it was to an 8-year-old kid without a mitt? I was on first base!

Now I was into my game. I started dancing – okay, maybe it was more like shuffling – off first bse just like Willie Mays, trying to steal second. That little fantasy vanished when I was informed there was no stealing in this game. You had to stay on base until the next batter actually hit the ball.

No matter. I was crouched and waiting for the crack of the bat, or at least a dull thud. Then a skinny 12-year-old hit a slow roller to the pig-tailed third baseman. I was off in a rather hitch-and-stagger gait that reflected my arthritic knees. I was sure I was going to make it. The second baseman was a six-year-old girl, and I figured she would drop the throw from third.

A funny thing happened on the way to second, however. The footwork got confusing. I don't know if I stubbed my toe or just tripped. The next thing I knew, I was laying flat on my stomach between first and second, my glasses broken, pants ripped, and knee bloodied.

I think the few onlookers thought I'd had a heart attack, so they rushed out to help me. As they helped me up, I was too busy trying to act nonchalant, brushing off the dust and muttering, "I'm OK."

With dignity shattered, I realized I had played my last ball game. I hobbled back to the bleachers – where I should have been all the time.

Pasture Pavarotti

There can be all kinds of culture clashes when city meets country. Solving them can be fun and easy when city and country friends get together, especially when they have a sense of humor.

The best way to understand each other's point of view is to rotate visits to both places, a case of we will come to your place if you will come to ours. We had our first taste of pizza in this manner when we went for a night out with our city friends. Living in East Aurora does have its restrictions when it comes to doing much more than porch sitting. We decided to give it a try when our city friends were due to come for their annual reciprocal visit.

We had been fortunate enough to visit the Sheldon Hotel years ago, long before it burned. In that day and age, a group of 10 or 12 people could pretty much establish the mood for the evening in one of these small rural hotels. Our group swept in and had a great party with delicious food, entertained by the proprietor and his wife. It was a classic visit to rural America and so the Sheldon Hotel became a place of fond memories.

The following year, when our city friends were due for their annual visit, we thought what better place than the Sheldon Hotel, with its well remembered mood, food, and memories? The four of us arrived for our night of action, greeted by a crowd of two thirsty locals washing down the dust accumulated by a day spent in the hay fields.

So much for the mood, although we still had the food and it was good. Lots of it, served family style. Meat, potatoes, gravy and apple pie, the all-American meal, and it compared favorably with pizza in the city. Just coffee and an after dinner drink and we would have showed our city friends what peaceful country living was all about.

Now imagine, if you can, a lovely summer evening , a cool breeze coming in through the open windows, a view of Lower Sheldon from High Sheldon, and the sun slowly setting over Dutch Hollow. There were even a few cows wandering around just outside the window, which added to this pastoral scene.

One curious cow, probably in a moment of bovine boredom, stuck its head in the window right at our friends' back. Being a cow, it did what cows do best: it mooed, loud and long! Our friends were slightly more than startled, not having seen the cow and never before having heard a Pavarotti of the Pasture.

Old Ace Moved the Bar

It took six men and a boy to move the bar during the latest remodeling of The Roycroft Inn, or so the story goes. The stories and deals that transpired there could fill volumes. But many years ago on a trout fishing trip, I first heard the story, as we sat around the camp fire, of how *one* man moved the bar.

In the late 1940s, all the boys who'd gone off to war had returned as men. We're talking "Men were Men" in the mold of John Wayne. They had survived a great war and years of separation from family and friends. Now was the time to get on with life and maybe relive some of war's heroics in the form of the rough-and-tumble cowboy movies they remembered seeing as kids at the Aurora Theater.

At this time, in the early 1950s, the Roycroft Bar was the place to meet, greet, and impress friends with war stories, to reminisce about formative years in East Aurora, and to drink. We can't say for sure that drink was the downfall of Old Ace, but he did enjoy a bottle or two with the old gang. His favorite spot was at the far end of the bar, far enough from the door so he didn't get interrupted by too much commotion, but with a good view of who was arriving, so he could pick and choose whom he wanted to talk to.

Unfortunately Ace had a few too many one night and the bartender decided one more would be way too much. Now, Ace was in the prime of his life, six-foot-four, a former three-letter man in high school, and a veteran of the South Pacific. In the image of John Wayne, Ace decided nobody was going to tell him what, when, or where he could drink. With the assurance of a hardened veteran, he made these facts known as he took his stand at the end of the bar.

Ace's next words were remembered as something like, "If you won't serve me in my own hometown, I'm going to pick up your bar." The challenge had been made and nobody, not even the bartender, made a move.

So, as the story goes, Old Ace sort of hunkered down, wrapped his arms around the bar just below the wide flat top, and stood up. Up went the bar for a few seconds. Was Ace tempted to tip over the whole unit, as John Wayne might have done? We will never know. Instead, he lowered it to the floor, dusted off his hands, and walked out.

Honor saved, dignity intact, and no harm done.

I Mopped the Floor With the Mayor

The "Black & White Ball" at the Knox Estate was a once-in-a-lifetime experience for any kid who grew up in East Aurora. For more than 70 years I had driven past this monument to old wealth. The estate had an ornate, iron-gated entrace and stood behind the stone wall that is the premier entrance to East Aurora.

Finally, in my 75th year, I had my chance to visit the mansion. Of course, the Knoxes had sold the estate and it is now part of the New York State Parks Commission. But it still has the grandeur of a bygone era, when estate living was just a fantasy of any small-town kid's imagination.

Our local Tourism Task Force had a fundraiser, thus the invitation. To be dressed properly, I bought a new black sweater to go with my black pants. A white shirt completed the ensemble and conformed with the Black-and-white theme. Not a style-setter for the vening, but hey, I was a local and they let me in!

The old manse looked pretty swell with special colored lights accenting the driveway and main entrance. Inside, it was wall-to-wall supporters of tourism, history buffs, curiosity seekers, some being-seen-by-the-being-seeners, and a few politicians.

The food was excellent, sort of modeled after A Taste of Buffalo, but with an East Aurora flavor. It wasn't exactly munching along Main Street, but with the the best from all our locally owned restaurants, it might be described as the Aura and Aroma of Aurora.

So, with a full stomach and a rich iced chocolate mocha in hand, I plunged into the crowd. There was the usual mix of butchers, bakers, candlestick makers, a few merchants, a mayor and maidens so fair, and we all mingled for an evening of fun.

In amongst the crowd, one person stood out. The mayor of Buffalo. Here was a once-in-a-lifetime chance to shake hands and talk with a man whom I had seen in the papers and on television, but never in person.

As I walked toward him, I had thoughts of mentioning Buffalo politics, or possibly telling him the history of East Aurora and all the benefits we enjoy as a result of living in a small town.

Then things got dicey! First, I had to switch my mocha to my other hand, in order to shakes hands. Then my thoughts turned to how I should address him. Should it be your honor or Mr. Mayor or Mr. Masiello or Tony?

No problem. The cup slipped and I poured my nice rich cup of whipped cream-topped mocha on his shoe, on the floor, and managing to splash some on myself as well.

The Mayor never missed a beat. He grabbed a fistful of napkins and helped me mop up. When I tried to apologize or asked him to let me clean up, his only remark was, "That's all right. I'm used to cleaning up messes."

Return of the Native

Return of the Native. Do you remember reading the book for high school English? I remember the title but not the plot, but it doesn't really matter. The title is the key, where after 50-plus years of working in the same place, a once-familiar name or face will occasionally reappear here in East Aurora.

It happened again, today, when a very attractive 70-ish little lady appeared in the store and announced that she was Dorcas Redman. Now Dorcas Martin, and widowed.

It is a real thrill, plus mixed emotions, when someone from out of your past reappears. The mixed emotions were a result of having assumed Dorcas had departed this mortal sphere. She had never responded to our more recent class reunions.

Anyhow, I told Dorcas I was truly glad to see her and if I knew her a little better I would have given her a big hug. She indicated that might be a good idea, so we talked some more and had our hug. We both realized that such a public display would not have been acceptable fifty years ago, as we were both too shy.

But by golly, now it was O.K. There are some advantages to living in the old home town and reaching the mature years, gracefully?

Porch Sitting

A gate left open between our yard and the neighbor's was better than a formal invitation. Today had been the first really hot day after a long winter. Unannounced, we stepped through the gate and, after a brief discussion about the heat, we all decided it was time to relax. They had the only front porch, so we agreed to meet there in ten minutes, just enough time for all of us to grab a glass or can of our favorite beverage, plus a chunk of cheese and some crackers.

Small-town front porches, particularly on Oakwood Avenue, are wonderful places to observe the passing parade. Also, to check up on the new neighbors' landscaping, house maintenance, and kids' activities. It didn't take long for the conversation/gossip to get serious. As with all gossip, accuracy was not as important as its entertainment value.

From around the corner, the familiar music of the ice cream van could be heard. The kids' activities came to a sudden halt. Scooters were dropped and there was a mad, screaming dash into the house to alert Mom of the approaching van, full of frozen delights. The youngest Mom in the neighborhood and the rest of her family appeared. Selections were

made and Mom was invited to join the porch sitters. She brought her own can of pop.

Neighbors' front porches were made for small towns and family living. This one, being across the street, was just far enough away for that youngest Mom to be removed from the bustle of her family but close enough to keep an eye and ear on the kids at home.

Perfect! The conversation flowed along with the occasional beer, wine, or pop. Instructions were shouted across the street as to how to create a school project that involved something called "Fudge-Apple" dessert. The other Porch-Sitting Mothers chimed in with their years of experience as to recipe, ingredients, cooking temperatures, and pan sizes.

Finally, the last Dad arrived home from work. The ice cream was gone but the stories just got better, and the school project was still in its formative stage. Meanwhile, cars and bicycles and walkers continued on their journeys through life here in East Aurora, and all was well in our part of the world.

About the Author

After over 50 years, Ed still works at the first, same, and only job he's ever had, at Vidler's 5 & 10. The consummate clerk, Ed feels that dealing with people is the greatest job in the world. The variety of folks that walk through his door never ceases to amaze him.

A resident of East Aurora since 1929, Ed still lives in the village with his wife, Pat. He can be found at Vidler's most days, working under the influence of his brother Bob, daughter Beverly, and nephew Cliff. Ed is not as swift of foot as he used to be, but after 450,000 times up and down the stairs and over 500 miles of swept floors he is still sweeping, smiling, talking, and occasionally listening.

These stories began as an ill-fated attempt to write a tourism brochure. With encouragement from Pat and a few friends, he was inspired to record the mirth, myths, and memories of a classic American small town. Ed is still inspired by the Life, People, and Laughter of the old hometown to write these tales.

About the Artist

Our artist, Bob Fisk, is a former Merchant Marine from Brooklyn. He attended the School of Visual Arts and married artist Sally Cook, whose painting of "Vidler's 5 & 10" is on display in the store.

Bob's cartoons have been displayed in a number of publications, most notably the military paper Stars and Stripes, where he was an advocate for the Vietnam Veteran, and at an exhibit at Central Michigan University in conjunction with his wife's work.

Bob says that in all his years sailing worldwide, he never heard sea stories that could compare to the ones Ed Vidler has collected about that sleepy little village, East Aurora.